GW01090351

Stop Trying to Be Perfect

AN ALLEGORY FOR THE VULNERABLE

Kim Douglas Hiltunen

TRILOGY CHRISTIAN PUBLISHERS

TUSTIN, CA

Trilogy Christian Publishers
A Wholly Owned Subsidiary of Trinity Broadcasting Network
2442 Michelle Drive
Tustin, CA 92780

Copyright © 2021 by Kim Douglas Hiltunen

Scripture quotations marked NIV are taken from the Holy Bible, New International Version®, NIV®. Copyright © 1973, 1978, 1984, 2011 by Biblica, Inc.TM Used by permission of Zondervan. All rights reserved worldwide. www.zondervan.com. The "NIV" and "New International Version" are trademarks registered in the United States Patent and Trademark Office by Biblica, Inc.TM

No part of this book may be reproduced, stored in a retrieval system, or transmitted by any means without written permission from the author.

All rights reserved, including the right to reproduce this book or portions thereof in any form whatsoever.

For information, address Trilogy Christian Publishing

Rights Department, 2442 Michelle Drive, Tustin, Ca 92780.

Trilogy Christian Publishing/ TBN and colophon are trademarks of Trinity Broadcasting Network.

For information about special discounts for bulk purchases, please contact Trilogy Christian Publishing.

Manufactured in the United States of America

Trilogy Disclaimer: The views and content expressed in this book are those of the author and may not necessarily reflect the views and doctrine of Trilogy Christian Publishing or the Trinity Broadcasting Network.

10 9 8 7 6 5 4 3 2 1

Library of Congress Cataloging-in-Publication Data is available.

ISBN 978-1-63769-384-1

ISBN 978-1-63769-385-8 (ebook)

Contents

"Does not wisdom call out?
Does not understanding raise her voice?
On the heights along the way,
where the paths meet, she takes her stand..."[1]

Acknowledgements

My deepest appreciation to my wife, Grace Karen Hiltunen, who is God's messenger of grace toward me. Thank you for cheering me through the mud and the muck, then up and over my mountains of ponderings. And thank you for just passing by when I sit staring outside.

Profound thanks to Mr. Floyd Long, posthumously, for praising my poetic recitation of a dying oak in his ninth-grade Creative Writing class fifty-two years ago.

To the woman who did not go beyond eighth grade but mastered Webster's Dictionary, the only book in her childhood home: Thank you, Mom, posthumously, for giving me a love for words.

To the many kind souls who patiently tromped along and advised through all that ultimately became this piece, my sincere thanks: Grace Karen Hiltunen, for loving me when I am a grump; Ron and Anita Shoemaker, for challenging my title choices; John Sztykiel, for stressing good sources; David Reynolds, for multiple helpful suggestions and writers' resources; and Lindsey Slivensky, for grammar checks and flow of the story. Special thanks to Gerald Alvaro for helping me to clarify what really matters.

To Michael Getzmiller and his dog, Polly, who crossed my path by God's perfect timing: Thank you, sir, for your cool decorum when I said you looked like the old man in my story and Polly looked just like the dog.

To my grown sons, Eric and Nathan: May God richly bless you for forgiving my excessive punctiliousness while you were growing up. I love you, and I am proud of you!

Are You Burning Out?

This allegory features Earnest and Clarity. Earnest is a perfectionist who is burning out, and Clarity is trying to help. She is late, but not too late. Many had watched the man burn and had said some things but did nothing more. So he kept on burning. You may be able to relate in one way or the other. You know that you are not alone.

The World Health Organization (WHO) defines burnout as:

"...a syndrome conceptualized as resulting from chronic workplace stress that has not been successfully managed. It is characterized by three dimensions:

- Feelings of energy depletion or exhaustion;
- increased mental distance from one's job, or feelings of negativism or cynicism related to one's job, and
- reduced professional efficacy."[2]

A cursory internet review will show that at least 20 percent of the American workforce is burned out. So it may even be the case that one in every five of your acquaintances has simply given up, either at work or at home or both. Too many people unnecessarily drag themselves along as wreckage among us.

The emotional toll is high, not only for the burned-out person but also for their family and friends, which will be developed in the course of this allegory. What is not addressed beyond a brief mention are the financial costs of burnout in the U.S. The basic breakdown follows. Stats are given for the whole population, then physicians, then nurses. Those two professions alone count for 16 percent. Also, note that this is pre-COVID, so we can safely assume the numbers to be significantly higher, especially in urban areas where the two waves of the pandemic killed so many and stressed care providers beyond their breaking points.

The Financial Cost of Burnout in the U.S.
Overall workforce: $190 billion per year.[3]
Physicians: $17 billion per year[4]
Nurses: $14 billion per year[5]

No one wants to burn out, and most of us, like Clarity, want to help our overworked or perfectionist friends. Or we may be the ones needing the help. The problem is that most of us do not know what to say if we are burning out or we do not have thought-out approaches for helping others. Maybe it is just a timing issue. Or we just talk ourselves out of it for the sake of avoiding confrontation. Meanwhile, the burning continues.

The premise in this allegory is that perfectionists are the most vulnerable to burnout. Perfectionism has historical roots. E.g., something embarrassing or catastrophic may have happened in the past. It may have resulted in punishment or even someone's death. To compensate, one might resolve to never be embarrassed again or cause anything catastrophic by doing *everything* just right.

So, over the years, the perfectionist's reputation is all about accuracy, especially of the quantitative sort. They commit to reliably hitting clearly defined goals, wherever they may be, and their accomplishments are obvious to all. But to get there, the perfectionist pores over the minutest details repeatedly so as to not miss a thing. An otherwise enjoyable job for them becomes a sort of bondage to unreality. Errors terrify them, so they work fiercely to stay safe.

But where perfectionism takes its greater toll is in the qualitative. Questions of optics are critical—looking right, acting right, saying just the right thing, creating the perfect presentation, avoiding offense at all costs, etc. Like someone with anorexia nervosa, stuck with an obese self-impression, the perfectionist struggling with quality is unable to see their work as good enough, much less "perfect." So re-work and re-working the re-worked product becomes an inescapable loop. Once the perfectionist is habituated, especially in the qualitative, it takes powerful persuasion to help them see the consequences of their self-slavery. Then, with those seen and with patient, diligent, and loving coaching, they are more likely to make the right decisions for the sake of their mental and physical health, but also for the health of all their relationships.

The margins in this story are wide for your notes. Significant themes are amplified in bold throughout, but you have space for your moments of epiphany.

Jesus said, "I have come that they may have life, and have it to the full."[6] May you be better equipped for the difficulties in your own journey as you read this, but may you also be one who, like Clarity, influences a perfectionist friend toward a healthier, fuller life.

1

Earnest

Earnest is the busiest person he knows. Every moment of every day is taken. Many moments of every night are as well—and not for sleep or pleasure. On weeknights, he is at his hospital office, where other leaders stop at day's end to be sure he is okay. He always smiles and says he is. But he is not. He somehow finds himself behind in everything: Policies and procedures are out of date; he is far afield from his budget—low revenues, high expenditures; his staff is frustrated because they feel as if their needs are not heard; vendor relations are strained; physicians' needs are not being met; patients want answers for issues relating to their care; equipment is broken down. His to-do list is endless, and everything feels like an emergency. He is unable to stay current with everything demanded of him. He has no peace.

To get caught up at work, Earnest's weekends are a blur—brief moments of transition, where he hurries home to shower and eat for an extended break. He then waves and smiles at his wife and kids as he hurries back to work. It feels wrong when he leaves his family behind for yet another evening. But he tells them this stretch of craziness will end soon and that it will not lead into another. But that has rarely happened for him. Big issues and little issues he made into big ones have always demanded his time. They are his excuse for all who watch him from the sidelines. He reminds them that he is critical to the success of his organization.

Earnest's phone is a light but deadly tether. It is never more than a couple feet away from him. He checks it over 2,000 times a day.[7] In fact, Earnest is afraid someone will not have his input for problems that could arise in his department. He fears he might miss a call. Always on his mind is a patient's life that could be at risk, and he feels personally responsible for everything to run smoothly. So the digital nanny holds him closely.

Superiors and colleagues marvel at Earnest. "You can do so much at the same time!" was the warm and frequent accolade—and, oh, it felt so good, so affirming! But then they give him more to do—especially committee involvements, because, after all, it is the busiest and most conscientious people with good reputations who get things done. Few are more conscientious than he. But his superiors and colleagues did not see the toxic brooding and placating that drove him to this point. The ruminations ad nauseum over his duties eventually got Earnest into a log jam, causing him to miss family and social events that mattered most to him. He was conflicted every day. It was not the prestige of accomplishment and admiration that drove him. It was an inordinate fear of losing his job—a visitation from his childhood of imminent punishment for mistakes. So he deceives himself by thinking more time at work equals more security. But stealing the time from family made them feel less secure.

"Generally, the more people ruminate, the less effective they are at problem-solving."[8]

Not a single accolade comes from his family. First of all, they really have no idea what his scope of responsibility is. Secondly, even if they knew, it would matter little because it keeps him from doing things with them during the time most husbands and fathers are home. To them, he is *awol*.

So Earnest's job is a thief. It steals his life. At day's end, he hauls his corpse home, flips off his shoes, and drops into his easy chair. After a nap, he nukes his dinner and eats it in a trance. Usually, no one is around because they all went to bed.

The kids' school events generally do not sync with Earnest's Outlook calendar. Before his current busyness, which started a few years ago, an occasional event would be missed. Now he occasionally attends one. People see him with his nose pointed at his phone. He is loyal to his company—no one doubts that—and is well-rewarded for it. The cash flows with the kudos. The appreciation feels more and more fantastic (especially since none comes from his family), so Earnest picks up his pace. Meanwhile, his wife and kids prepare for mutiny.

A family intervention is attempted but ends with the front door slamming and his tires screeching as he flees from everyone's pain. But he cannot run from his own. He is in a trap and does not see how to break free.

The family hates Earnest's job. He loves his family, but he feels entombed by the laurels of his success, which will not transfer should he land another job. The thought of leaving the great pay makes his stomach burn. Otherwise, leaving the position would not be a problem. He fears being unable to provide for his family. If only they could see his obsession with work as evidence of how much he loves them! But they want him to see how starved they are for his love! They all need to see that he and his family were all starving for love. Then they can get help once they understand what caused all this.

All of his physicians say that Earnest's health is deteriorating due to his work-related stress. He knows he needs exercise, but he has no time for it. Meetings in the mornings and evenings and weekends have buried his workout calendar. He grabs fast food before or after these obligations; the faster, the better. Then he rewards himself with fresh pastries and shakes. They ease the burning in his stomach.

Looking in his mirror, Earnest sees how overweight he is. The irony of it: He is a healthcare professional, yet totally out of shape! Any health-related counsel he offers is given with the disclaimer that his "loss of tone" is temporary. He does not qualify "temporary" as lasting for five years. So patients politely nod while wondering why he has failed to maintain himself.

He has considered how he could lose weight. But after a week of effort, the burning in his stomach worsens. The medicine he takes fails to control it. So he drops the diet and picks up more food, which seems to help the medicine work better. Mass may accrue on the outside, but at least there is no burning inside.

Earnest briefly tries alcohol, but it makes his stomach worse. Illicit drugs are only a brief thought. He considers how awful it would be for the wife and kids if he were arrested.

A pile of medications fills his cabinet. The overflow is in a kitchen cupboard. Each broken-down part gets a pill: chronic neck pain, low thyroid function, lack of digestive enzymes, high blood pressure, and a heart disorder. Vitamins and minerals compensate for his poor eating habits. Well, in his mind, they do.

"Some studies have found that high blood pressure is more prevalent among perfectionistic people, and other researchers have even linked the trait with cardiovascular disease."[9]

Meanwhile, in real life, the hamster wheel of his job flies faster while the plates he spins are dropping around him. Earnest sees the diminishing returns of his pace and knows he is actively burning out. His medicine cabinets and comfort foods fail to make anything better.

Others have watched him over the years. His transition from joyful colleague to poser was within a year of taking his new job. He was a captive to his own brokenness and could not call out for help.

At the beginning, Earnest was ready for this job. It dovetailed with his academic and clinical training as well as his personality. But in subtle ways, because he was so vulnerable, work became a gooey flypaper. Friends and colleagues told him to be sure to take vacations and not be "so out-of-balance." But he ignored them. The hospital needed him, he said, and he would make it up eventually with his family and friends. But the family is trying its best to live without him now, and his friends are falling away into the past. He needs his full energy for work, he says. "Fine," they all say, "go for it." In time, he becomes accustomed to being alone. But as he was heading into total burnout, it seemed too late for anyone to help. And those who had the ability to help were themselves beset with high-stakes demands, the triage of which set their most urgent issues ahead of Earnest's.

One day, he decides to walk to the hospital, which is near his home. He had driven before because it was faster, but today, he needs thinking time. He had left early enough, and no one in the house is awake yet.

When he was healthy, he walked faster, with purpose. But his stride is shorter and slower this particular morning for the sake of his aching knees. The pace helps as he ponders how he got to where he is now and what to do next.

2

At Risk

Earnest stops at a gate overgrown with evergreens. Until this moment, it did not exist. Year after year, he quickly walked past it, pensive and worried. Everything and everyone outside his job was grey and irrelevant.

But suddenly, somehow, color and beauty redirect his focus. Beyond the evergreen arch is a tall, luminous forest. Perfectly straight and topped with spreads of gold and hints of red, deciduous giants show off in the morning sun. Stands of deep green ferns contrast themselves below where leaves had fallen onto a peaceful canvas.

Soon Earnest is drawn to the scent of pines in the cool, fall wind. It comes in waves, surging now as he wants to be on the golden-brown pathway beyond the gate.

The street noise fades behind him—the crazy, squeaky horns, bossy horns, jackhammers, whistles, shouts, and sirens. Brakes are screeching, and yellers are yelling. Walkers walk by, each denying it all with earbuds. Exhaust fumes fill the air; the bakeries cannot compete. A low-flying plane briefly blocks the sun, its roaring engines blending with the cacophony.

Earnest is tense from thinking about what is ahead today. Many deadlines. Sour people. Tasks undone. Unmet boss's expectations. Family sadness. His own sadness. Same job, same routine. An occasional, fleeting happy moment—oh, that there could be more! The brief hugs, then goodbyes, and more goodbyes. Sad kids. A very sad wife. Relief from it all seems so far away, even impossible. He wants to turn it all off.

This happens every day. Every. Single. Day. Except today. Earnest knows he risks losing valuable time, but he opens the gate and steps onto a soft path.

The trail is quiet. In a few steps, it absorbs the tonnage of Earnest's angst. In fact, Crazyville has now become irrelevant. The land of the dying is now behind him.

Sunlight was never so radiant as Earnest looks all around while the singers of the forest dance among the high branches. He thinks back to when he was a kid, playing in the forest by his home—the tree forts and sapling catapults and tripwires set for *the enemy*. But he has no enemies here. And his stomach does not burn.

He slowly takes it all in as he walks along, passing through the deciduous forest, then melding with quiet, majestic pines. Their scent at the gate was a tease that soon yields to the earthy and composted smell of deep wilderness. Windfalls abound, their dark, twisted roots splayed in all directions. Earnest watches and hears the songbirds as he eats berries, strolling for what seem to be miles of curves, knolls, and rocky streams. He recalls the few peaceful moments of his childhood, where he retreated from abusive parents.

His father was more about tasks than people. That is, when he was not drunk. He was a carpenter, fastidious with every detail. Earnest could not help in his dad's workshop because the carpenter had no patience with him. In the time it would take to show Earnest how to do something, he could do it himself. And he was too busy, anyway, and often grumbled about it. So Earnest reasoned that there was nothing he could do or say to please his father—unless he excelled in school. If he made all A's, his father commented, "Good job." B's and C's were not addressed, and rarely was there much discussion. Dad's expectations were high, his affirmations few, so Earnest stayed out of his way.

However, when Dad was drunk, he was jolly and effusive with the boy. They would even play catch or wrestle. But at an early age, he saw that there was something plastic about Dad's friendliness because it was absent when he was sober. His ups and downs were as predictable as weekends and Mondays. Eventually, Earnest was plastic in return but dreaded the wrathful Mondays. He became a chameleon to survive.

Earnest's mother drank socially at first, then tipped a fifth on her own every day. In an instant, an amiable moment for his parents became a brawl at the change of either one's mood. Earnest could not protect his mother—he was too little and too scared of the fury of slaps and slamming doors. His father's beatings were weekly, the victim being either Mom or Earnest or both. But Mom would often suddenly turn on Earnest and abuse him verbally or physically. Dad held no solace in a home that became a trap. So, as often as he could, he retreated to the nearby forest, away from Camels, Seagrams, and terrifying surprises.

When he was only five, Earnest learned perfectionism. His mother had chided him relentlessly about how
disorganized his toys were. When he quickly respond-
ed, aligning, stacking, and collating them in straight
rows, she praised him. So his toy area was tidy forev-
ermore, and he learned the conditions of love. Early
on, perfection in all things had wonderful results. The
optics were all that mattered.

Because Mom was often drunk, Earnest had to clean
the house every week. It was a modest-sized home. But
Mom demanded spotlessness everywhere. And no play
was allowed until the dishes were done and the house
was cleaned. If she found no dust, he was praised and
allowed to play, sometimes with friends, but mostly in
his room or his yard—alone.

When he was twelve, mowing their half-acre lawn
and cleaning the house was expected every week. Both
had to be perfect. When they were, Earnest was praised
and given an allowance. Neighbors complimented his
mom for the tidy home she kept. But it was Earnest's
personal success; he wanted them to see her as *normal*.
When they saw him in the yard, they noted his fine lawn
work. It was love to him—and he loved to be loved by his
neighbors. Rewards for perfection were everywhere.

To Earnest, it was like being in heaven when he
made something look good, and the accolades came.
While they were not the same as loving affirmations of

him as a person, he felt loved nonetheless and started to identify with his work: he was the work, and the work was him. Perfectionism was his brand and praise his currency. It was his key to survival. Excellence and extreme diligence eventually worked for him in the military, professional schooling, and healthcare. Whatever he did, it was perfect or it was nothing. If it was nothing, so was he.

"Inauthentic and perfectionistic behaviors are believed to develop in childhood. The child ultimately disregards their intrinsic needs and desires and instead devotes their energy to meet the needs and expectations of others. They are hypervigilant to what is needed to gain a sense of belonging. They learn that with their achievements and performance comes love, praise, and affection. And this lesson stays with them throughout life."[10]

But now he is in the forest, where no one knows him and where he does not have to perform. Casually strolling, he savors the fresh air and freedom.

Earnest finds a bench along the path and lies down. The warped wood and slats were not uncomfortable. Through the dense treetops, he looks deeply into the sky, so blue, so clean, so perfect. Content and peaceful, he falls asleep.

3

Clarity

Earnest regales the locals with snoring. Blue jays quietly watch from above while two chipmunks dash through the leaves around the bench. The more curious one dares to jump onto Earnest's arm, then sprint across to the other and back to the ground. His chum watches from a hollow log.

Someone approaches Earnest and stands beside him. The person draws closer, and Earnest hears gentle breathing. As it gets louder and warmer on his face, he opens his eyes.

He jumps up, and a little girl jumps back. But he is more surprised than she.

With soprano pitch, she chirps, "Hi, Earnest! Welcome!"

"To what? Where? Who are you? How do you know me?"

She lets him sputter a moment. She is only four feet tall, but beams confidence with shoulders back, chin up, and a dimpled smile. She is cheery, but he is not, and his eyes widen, then scrunch in a scowl.

She knows his name! But where are her parents?

"My name is Clarity," she says, with a half step toward him. "And I've been sent to you." She looked all of seven years old, healthy and well-groomed.

She stares, awaiting Earnest's response. Flustered, he is unable to form one, so she takes over.

"You're going through some trouble, aren't you?"

"Why would it matter to you? I don't even know you. You're just a little kid—what, seven?"

"Seven-and-a-half, going on eight," she retorts as she stands on her toes to look taller. "I want to help you."

"You think you can help me?"

"Yup." She flips her hair, then puts her hands on her hips.

She continues, "A while ago, you were in your usual, crazy life. In fact, your family and friends knew it was crazy. You knew it was crazy. So I want to help you."

Clarity proves that she knows about Earnest. From date, time, and place of birth to the present moment, she tells him his life story while twisting her hair and balancing herself on the edge of his bench. She is wiry and agile, bowing toward him while on one foot with the other high in the air behind her.

"I still can't believe it. You're just a little girl."

"Sounds like you're stuck." She tilts her head to one side and, with a serious look, leans toward Earnest and looks into his eyes while one foot is still high in the air. "I have something to tell you that will save your life."

"Oh, really?" he doubtfully drolls. He asks, "How long will it take? When will we be done?"

"Depends on how you respond to what I'm going to show you."

4

On the Path

Clarity stops her playfulness and sits next to Earnest, not losing eye contact..

"So?"

"So what?" he replies.

"So you wanna let me show you some things as we walk along the path?"

He thinks about all this coming from a kid. Then Clarity whistles. Darting from bushes nearby is a scruffy and happy five-pound mutt who jumps onto her lap. "Well, who's this?" Earnest asks.

"This is R.D. He's a rescue," she says, rubbing his ears and cooing. He turns to lick her nose.

"Oh? From where?"

"My parents adopted him from a shelter."

"Wonderful! A rescue!"

"Yup, he's a rescue, just like you."

"Oh. Sure." He scrunches his brow again.

"Wanna go?" she persists.

Earnest relents. "Okay."

"Great! Let's go," Clarity says, already on the path.

"So what does R.D. stand for?" Earnest asks, trying to keep up with her quick little steps.

"Rescue Dog."

"Oh, well, after what we just talked about, I thought it would be something really profound."

"Nope," she replies. "I like to keep things simple."

"Of course. Yup. We're keeping it simple."

"Yup. Okay, we've got a lot to see. Let's go." She motors along a couple of strides ahead of Earnest.

"To where?"

"You'll see. And you'll love it."

"But, meanwhile, let's talk about your job—where you were going when you stopped at the gate. It's the biggest stressor of your life now, right?" She slows for him to walk alongside her.

"Looks like your job has taken over your soul. You can't leave work at work, so you take it home with you, right? But your family doesn't like your hospital being in the house with them. They just want you! Do you realize that?"

The confrontation catches Earnest by surprise. Normally it would come from an adult—like a therapist or a really close friend—not a stranger, especially one who is a little kid whom he just met.

"You know what? You're burning out," Clarity says. "And here's how I know:

- You're a perfectionist! You won't let yourself be less than perfect. The optics make your work look great, but you look awful!
- You're exhausted at the end of your workday.
- You isolate yourself.
- You have escape fantasies—and have thought about escaping through death, even suicide.
- You're a grump with your family—always irritable with your kids.
- You have so many illnesses.[11]

"But it didn't happen all of a sudden. You went through the usual twelve stages:

1. Excessive drive or ambition: You jumped in with heart and soul. You were thrilled with this job!

2. Pushing yourself to work harder: That was your habit—perfectionism has been in you since you were a kid.

3. Neglecting personal care and needs: How about that gut?

4. Displacement of conflict: You pinned your work-aholism on others or on situations. You didn't take personal responsibility for being so driven.

5. No time for non-work-related needs: When was your last day for just you and your family?

6. Denial: You've been plugging along, not seeing that you're going to pot!

7. Withdrawal: You think no one understands any-way, so you're going it alone now.

8. Behavioral changes: You're more aggressive and irritable.

9. Depersonalization: You're no longer in control of your life, so you mentally detach yourself from it.

10. Inner emptiness or anxiety: No sense of gain for all your effort.

11. Depression: You see yourself in a hopeless situation.

12. Mental or physical exhaustion or collapse: You're not here yet. But you're not far from it!" [12]

Earnest sighs. "Yeah, I guess I'm deeper in this hole than I thought I was. I should've taken their cues seriously. My wife and kids don't talk to me. They explained it once: 'You don't have time for us.' You know, it really hurts to hear that. It's like I'm in a pit and can't climb out of it."

They stood looking at each other. Earnest is ashamed to say these things. What is worse is that this kid, the same age as one of his own, is calling him out.

"You can't start over by rewinding the clock to recover what you lost. But you can *choose* to get out of your pit. You really can have a life where your work has its right portion of your time in order to *let* you be healthy and enjoy the relationships you had messed up and missed out on. [13] You know the importance of the people in your life. And you're starting to get a sense of how many people you wounded by showing what appeared to be more love for your work than for them—even though that really wasn't the case, but that's how they felt."

"Being realistic, it may mean telling yourself that you have given enough to your company. You need to look at all your options, which might mean lowering your standard of living in order to increase the joy of it by being involved in what matters most. [14] But thinking forward to your deathbed, do you think you will wish you had more money and things? Or do you suppose you'll wish you had more time with those you loved?"

"Consider these options, generally least drastic to the most:

- For starters, you may be able to redesign how you do your work by:
  - o *Eliminating nonessentials.* Some things you shouldn't have to do at all. So get rid of them.
  - o *Automating.* A simple example is your schedule: You plan to do certain things at certain times—automatically. It can be more complicated after that, but whatever you can automate will work in your favor.
  - o *Delegating to someone else.* Look at all you do. Can some of the workload be spread around to others?
  - o *Procrastinating.* Yup, that's a legitimate decision. Some things don't have to be done way in advance but can wait. You just don't want to wait too long—so put it on your calendar!
  - o *Concentrating* on what is a priority. All the other concepts are to free you for the purpose of concentrating on what is the most important matter now.[15]

- Talk to your peers. Have they been overwhelmed? How have they worked through it? Maybe their advice will work for you.
- Ask yourself, "What is the truth about my situation?" You might be all amped up emotionally, but when you step back, you'll get a better perspective.
- Talk to a therapist or a pastor. Ask them to think through your situation with you. Another set of eyes can see things from the outside that you don't see inside your life. We'll talk more about helpers and coaches later.
- If the above people tell you to consider other options, look at what your marketable skills are, and check the want ads.
- If your skills are only marketable for where you are, and you're getting a sense, especially from the counsel of others, that you need to move on, think about what you'd want to try next. Then look at who provides the training.
- Look within your organization at what would be reasonable transfers for your skillset.
- Quit—preferably after having another job lined up. You need to maintain a cash flow. This is an extreme option to consider carefully. But if it becomes a choice between your life and your job, the job has to go."

"Actually, those who truly love you—the people you *really* want in your life—don't give a rip about any prestige you might have had. They just want you back. They love the unique person that is *you*. And those who truly love you, well, they feel bad when your work is the master of your soul. But they can't reach into your life and help you out of the pit you dug for yourself unless you let them. And that's super-hard if you're a perfectionist."

As Clarity finishes, they come upon a vast, overgrown cemetery. Some of the old grey markers are crosses; a few are Stars of David. Many are in pieces on the ground, having been broken by vandals. The stately, large obelisks with surnames prominently etched on them tell whose remains lie below.

Solemnly Clarity states, "My daddy is buried here. See his black granite stone way over there? It still looks brand new."

"He died at work. They found him on the floor of his office. They said it was a heart attack. His doctors had warned him that he needed to dial back on his work. He had blood pressure issues, and he was a diabetic."

"He played with us only once in a while. We loved when he carried us on his shoulders, when we played hide and seek, and when he wrestled with my brother. But that would be only on the holidays when his boss—and even his staff—would tell him he should be home with his family. Those were our happy times. But we really wanted more of them with him."

Clarity seemed almost indifferent as if she was over her loss. Earnest quietly says, "Oh, Clarity, I'm sorry!"

"He was supposed to be home a little early for Mom's birthday, but she was getting used to not expecting him to keep his promises. She didn't even plan for him to be home for dinner, so she didn't set a place for him at the table. Sure enough, he didn't come home because he had died while working in a hospital that saves lives. But it wasn't the hospital's fault. He was a perfectionist and had trouble leaving his work at work. He struggled to see when enough was enough."

"He had died while working in a hospital that saves lives."

"Anyway, his door was open, so when the janitor went to check it, she found him."

"My older brother said that, even before I was born, Dad was always at work or doing chores around the house. He had to do, do, do, whatever the task was because everything had to be in order or caught up. He was very smart, and everyone liked him. He worked really hard to be the best. But he didn't work very hard at being our dad."

"He worked really hard to be the best. But he didn't work very hard at being our dad."

"He promised to go to my brother's first cross-country meet the month before he died. Ethan looked for him on the course, but he didn't see him because he never came. He didn't come to the rest of Ethan's meets that month. He had an important project, he told him, thinking he would understand."

"Way back a few years ago, on my first day of kindergarten, Mom had a little party for me. She said Dad would be there. But he texted from his office: A meeting was called at the last minute, and he had to attend. We thought he'd be late. Well, he finally came home, but it was after Mom tucked me in late that night."

"Mom *really* yelled at him. She said, 'When did you marry the hospital? And I wasn't invited! In fact, you have done nothing with me and our children for the past year! You've got a great job? Does 'great' mean you're a great doormat?' He yelled back that she should've been thankful that she didn't have to work."

"So, because they were yelling at each other, Ethan and I couldn't sleep. They were so loud, and they said terrible things about each other. But it wasn't just that night. They fought often. Sometimes Dad just stormed out of the house when it really got bad. Nobody knew where he went, though he eventually came home around midnight. We were scared that they were going to end up divorced."

"One night, he surprised Mom by coming home early, but he forgot it was their anniversary—so, no card, no gift—nothing. Mom slammed pots and pans around, then went to bed crying. Dad made our supper: hot dogs and beans. He was a terrible cook."

"Both of us kids just stared at our food as Dad washed the dishes, then went to his easy chair. He didn't even sit with us. We were starting to feel like a bother to him. But we especially felt bad for mom. We picked at the food because we weren't hungry. We just wanted our mom and dad to love each other."

"We both talk about Dad's death and feel guilty about it. Friends of ours are going through the same thing because their dad was also a perfectionist who died at his job."

Earnest stares at Clarity, then down at the path. He thinks to himself, *That could be me.* But what she quietly says next stops him cold: "My dad worked for you."

5

Readiness

Clarity's story was a gut punch. Earnest is dumbstruck, then carefully looks at her dad's name chiseled into the black granite and stutters, "Oh, Clarity, I-I am so, so sorry!"

They both cry. She embraces him with a vise-grip squeeze, the kind she could no longer give her own father, then steps back and recomposes herself.

This is so awkward for Earnest. Not only is he responsible for the pit in which he finds himself, but he feels as if he had killed one of his own managers—the father of this dear child.

Earnest drops to the path and sobs, with hands to his face, rocking back and forth. The burning in his stomach is a violent furnace. "Oh, what a mess I've created! Oh, what a mess! To think that my own obsessive work style flowed over to your dad, and he felt like he had to overwork himself to please me! Oh, Clarity, look at what I've done to you and your mom and your brother and to my own family! I'm so, so sorry! *Please* forgive me!"

Crying again, she touches his shoulder to console him.

"I forgive you—even though you really don't need me to—because it's not your fault what happened to my dad. He couldn't say no to your demands because he was afraid you'd fire him. And he refused to get help when my mother and his friends told him to. He wanted to work things out, thinking he was smart enough. But he couldn't get outside himself to fix the stuff he fought with on the inside. He was then like you are today. I couldn't help him, but maybe I and others can help you. I think you're ready for it."

"He couldn't get outside himself enough to fix the stuff he fought with on the inside."

"Ethan and I forgave our dad. Mom's working on it. You need to know that your wife and your children will forgive you if you sincerely apologize, admit you need help, and then, most importantly: *get the help!* You might've done the first one or two, but it's the last one that really counts."

"Your kids will easily forgive you. That's the way kids are. But your wife? Well, it might take some time to earn her trust back. You need to show all of them that you are getting the help you need."

"And here's the truth: People are professionally trained to encourage you and let you determine who you want to be as a husband and a father. They're the ones who will help you succeed. They have the tools, and they will give you the tools you need."

Earnest stands up, embarrassed. He wipes his eyes. His pride is broken, his stomach is burning, and he just wants to go home. He wants to hug his wife and kids and tell them he will be a new man. He is ready for help.

He mentions vulnerability as his biggest challenge, to which Clarity says, "Hey, those who understand will be good to you; but you have to *let* them help you. You have to talk to them so they can. Otherwise, left to your own devices, you risk plopping over dead."

"Left to your own devices, you risk plopping over dead."

"Earnest, leaders don't want their people burning out. Unfortunately, they often have their own plates so full that, by the time help is needed—like in your case— a struggling person is already burned out and unable to continue their work. Or, if it's not a full plate for a leader, it could be any of a number of other reasons that the struggle isn't taken seriously. In a way, it's kind of a compliment for you—that, as a perfectionist and work-aholic, you've pulled through tough times before and that this is seen as just another one of those times. But it isn't. Hopefully, all leaders learn about burnout and see the progression I mentioned in the twelve stages. Besides, while it emotionally affects them, it has a significant financial impact as well. Recruiting and training replacements is expensive."

They stop to sit on a fallen tree at the edge of the path. Clarity says, "I'll be back in a moment." She leaves him pondering as she runs a few paces into a brushy area to pluck up a random weed, pick it to pieces, sing something, then weave the pieces together as she returns and sits on a little stump in front of Earnest.

She blithely toggles to playfulness while he watches. He is amazed that she holds no grudge against him.

She lays her handiwork on a mossy patch of ground. "A friend taught me how to do it. It's a grasshopper bed."

R.D. then rushes out of the bushes and jumps onto Earnest's lap as if to console him. And it works.

6

The Summit

Back on the path, Clarity leads Earnest up an abrupt-ly steep hill, where the path narrows and quickly thins to nothing. With the strides and grabs of a seasoned hiker, Clarity grapples upward among several saplings and stony ridges. Earnest follows ineptly and struggles not to complain.

As he was about to ask for a break, they step onto a large granite outcropping. "Almost there," she says. She watches him as he pauses to catch his breath, then they continue upward.

The pitch of the climb lessens as they approach a hilltop—a treeless, mossy plateau. More than that, it is a wonderland to Earnest as he looks around.

Clarity lets him wow about it all. To the north is an ocean; its waves gently roll over the nearby beach at the base of the plateau. Gulls soar in the foreground as the silvery-blue expanse meets the sky in a distant thin line. Whales randomly launch, then land in splashes of thunder. The air is rich with a salty, humid smell.

To the south, a sheer-sided mountain stands starkly majestic against a blue sky. Earnest feels stared down by its granite face. A stratus cloud drifts across an imaginary neckline. "We're so tiny here," he says.

Clarity interrupts his reverie to look eastward, across a wide valley ready for harvest. A quilt of green and gold, the farms are stitched by fencerows, tree lines, and streams. A rivulet threads toward a lake, where confetti-like sailboats dance along with the valley breeze. "Looks like freedom," says Earnest. Clarity smiles.

Earnest's wonder is paused when Clarity shows him a quaint feature on the western edge of the plateau: an abandoned cabin with a barren covered porch. A ribbon of smoke rises from the chimney. The smell of burning cherry wood calls them inside.

"It's for you," Clarity says.

"For me? Up here? In the middle of all this? In the middle of nowhere? Why?"

"It's a place for you to recover."

"Food?"

"You'll have it."

"And my cell phone?"

"Won't need it."

"What's the purpose?"

"To feel God's majesty around you, to hear His voice, to recover from your crazy-hurried life, to enjoy His creation, His mercy, and especially His elaborate, un-yielding, and healing love for you. Besides—about the phone: You haven't yet learned that it's a tool, not an-other master. So, no phone because, well, there's also no signal."

They step onto the porch, and Earnest raises the latch. The hinge on the left groans as the door opens. He steps onto an old plank floor, softly aged and too worn to creak. From a small west window on his left, hazed hues of sunlight beam into an austere, well-lived space. Nothing is hanging on the walls of trim-cut logs. He runs his hand along them; not a draft anywhere. A kerosene lamp chatters on a table behind the door. Small flames lightly crackle in an iron stove as they peek through the sooty streaks of its glass. As if a duet, they both welcome Earnest for the night.

But, most surprising to him was what he saw next. As he entered, he didn't see the bed by the door. So when he turned around, he noticed: It was his own! "Why this?" he asks.

"Sometimes God just surprises us with amazing blessings after we have been through hell."

"Sometimes God just surprises us with amazing blessings after we have been through hell."

"But I don't have a stove or a fridge."

"Right," says Clarity. "You don't need them."

"But you said I'd have everything I need."

"You will."

"So, how's that going to happen if nothing is in here?"

"You'll see."

They stop talking briefly, then Earnest whispers, "I like it here. I think I need this."

Clarity replies, "I'll be back in the morning," and leaves.

Earnest is now alone in the middle of nowhere as long shadows give way to a moonless night. The lamp and the stove provide light and heat, but neither needs any tending. The hours pass as Earnest becomes hungry and starts to worry. "I need food. But how will I get it?" He grabs the lantern, steps onto the porch, and looks into the darkness. Then he turns to a little table by the door.

"What?" His lantern reveals a large, silver serving tray with a baroque-handled cover, so he takes it, puts it on the inside table, and stares at it. Then, lifting the cover, he sees his favorite dinner and beverages served on fine china and crystal with silver and gold utensils, all set as for a formal dinner. A linen napkin under the utensils was monogrammed with his initials.

No one had knocked to announce the gift. But Earnest was glad for it and began to eat.

In moments a little hand taps on the door. He opens it and sees Clarity in the lamplight.

"Oh, you got it!" she says. "Great! See how God knows your needs without your mentioning them? Enjoy the meal! See you in the morning! We have a big day ahead of us!"

She steps away into the darkness. Earnest is concerned for her safety, then says to himself, "If God is taking care of me like this, He'll take care of her out there."

"I am the LORD your God who brought you up out of Egypt. Open wide your mouth, and I will fill it."[16]

After dinner, Earnest gathers everything together and sets it on the porch. He already anticipates breakfast. "Weird, but I'll go with it," he says, as he readies himself for a night's rest. No longer hungry, he is warm and peaceful as the quiet duet lulls him to sleep.

Tides of dreamwork ebb and flow, when suddenly it devolves into vicious nightmares. The difficult people from Crazyville become monstrous and combative. In social settings, Earnest is partially dressed and mocked for it. He gets fired for the errors of others and has no recourse. His closest friends betray him. He drives into a parked car whose occupants swarm onto his new vehicle with hammers, screaming and crashing his windows. He is openly mocked as a failure in a high-level meeting. Debtors loudly harass him, pounding on his office window. In the end, he is chased off a cliff and tumbles into an abyss. "Help me!" he cries, then bolts upright in sweaty tremors.

His bedding is soaked and scrambled from thrashing. He looks around the room but sees nothing different. Relieved, he lay back down. Then Earnest hears a voice: "Your nightmare life is behind you. Hope is coming. Sleep in peace."

"He who forms the mountains creates the wind, and reveals his thoughts to man, he who turns dawn to darkness, and treads the high places of the earth—the LORD God Almighty is his name."[17]

7

Beholding

Bam-bam-bam! This time, Clarity had the knock of a burly man. Startled, Earnest jumps from his bed to open the door, but only a crack. "Did you have to pound so hard?"

"Breakfast is here!" she chimes in a "ta-da!" sort of way as if she sprang from a trampoline. She is all perma-fresh and full of energy. From the porch table, she presents another larger silver platter, this time with servings for two.

Earnest opens the door, and she enters to set the table—again, with china, crystal, silver, and gold, just like last night. She sits and starts to chatter. As if whiplashed, Earnest rubs his neck, then takes a moment to sit back on his bed. "What time is it?"

"Doesn't matter. Time to get up, talk about last night, and see a few more things before we're done. But let's eat first."

The cabin was warm all night as the fire kept going. The morning sun through a dusty east window gives enough light to eclipse the petite guest. Earnest reports having slept well, better than ever before.

He joins Clarity at the table and drinks his juice.

"You look better today," she says, after a bite. "How come?"

"I don't know," he replies. "Maybe because I had my own bed and pillow. But I had a lot of nightmares."

"Do you remember them?"

"Some of them. They were mostly about my fears."

"Okayyyy?"

"Well, they were horrible! I broke out in a sweat and woke up, and my sheets were all wet. But then a voice told me that all these things have passed, hope is coming, and to go to sleep—and I did! But the comment, 'Hope is coming,' comforted me. Now I'm stumped about what that hope is."

They finish breakfast, and both are quiet and content. Then Clarity gets up. "Okay, let's go," she says.

"Go? Where now? Don't we have to clean up or anything?"

"Nope. Let's go. I'll be outside." She unlatches the door and goes out, just beyond the porch. Earnest quickly looks at every detail inside the cabin, knowing he had to be here and not wanting to forget the experience. Wondering what this day will bring, he slowly steps out to join Clarity. The air is cool in the morning breeze. He squints at the sun, rising over the valley. The ocean calmly rolls toward the shore. The sheer wall of the imposing mountain welcomes the sun to warm its face. Not a cloud anywhere. Earnest senses that something good is about to happen.

"Okay, now what?"

"Take a moment to look at that mountain. How does it affect you?"

He quickly says, "Well, I feel so tiny."

"So, you know, just as God can do anything with this mountain, so He can do anything with the mountains in your life. Those troubles at work or with family and friends or at home—whatever they are, you can hand them over to Him. Besides, it's His job to help us with stuff like that, being God and all."

"Cast your cares on the LORD, and he will sustain you..."[18]

"For nothing is impossible with God."[19]

She continues, "Too often you thought you were smart enough to solve your own issues, not only in your work but in your whole life, as if you could handle them all by yourself, when, in fact, you knew deep down that you couldn't. So, while the helpers in your life can help you think through it all, you have to let them, like we talked about yesterday."

"Look at the valley down there—all those farms and the lake way out there.

"Yeah. It's so beautiful, like a massive work of art," says Earnest

"So, again, a Creator God and a tiny you..."

Earnest replies, "Right, assuming a caring, Creator God made all this, I'm starting to believe that He can take care of me and my problems without my worrying over them."

"Yes! Yes, we are making that assumption—that there is a personal God Who cares about us. We don't need to prove He exists. He already took care of that by what we see around us, what we know in our hearts, and what we're told by people He sends to us—like I was sent to you."

Clarity claps her hands. "Okay—you got it! But, for good measure, look over there."

Earnest turns toward the ocean.

"And?" probes Clarity.

"Again, majesty, immensity, horizon to horizon."

"And?"

"He can help me with my oceans full of problems."

"So what does that do to your fears?"

"Looking at all this," admits Earnest, "they're like nothing. I let myself get worked up over them."

"Okay, yup, you get it. You've *let* challenges grow into massive problems, and you let them wash over you and knock you down. You lost perspective, *letting* them consume your thought life," says Clarity, as she turns toward a path that leads down from the plateau. "There's more," she says.

Then she chirps, "You know what?"

"What?"

"In that cabin and out here, you encountered God."

"I thought so."

"Yup. He's the One Who basically told you, 'I got this.' Then He confirmed it by giving you an amazingly peaceful sleep. That's because God is all about doing what's amazing."

"Also, your fancy dinner and breakfast? You needed food, but He gave you much more. That's what His grace and mercy are like. And, when we hunger to know Him, wow! Watch what He does! But it's our choice. He wants us to want Him.

"In the middle of all this, He gives you more proof by showing you His creative power. This whole experience is meant just for you, Earnest—to show you how very precious you are to Him."

"You had been seeking truth, looking everywhere. You knew you were in trouble, living a driven, self-important life, needing to be perfect, so you finally called out to Him. Here's the truth: Every sincere seeker of God—like you—eventually finds Him, but not always in the expected places. You didn't expect to meet Him when you met me. I'm just a kid, but He used me as His messenger, who, in my simple faith, walks close to Him.

"Ask, and it will be given to you; seek and you will find; knock, and the door will be opened to you. For everyone who asks receives; he who seeks finds; and to him who knocks, the door will be opened."[20]

"And, you know what? You can have the same experience I'm having. You see, I learned that Jesus is intimate with God the Father and that I could have that same intimacy. I wanted it, asked for it, and now I have it. When God sees that desire in a person's heart, He responds. Usually, He responds by sending people to tell us about Jesus."

"Seek the LORD while he may be found; call on him while he is near."[21]

"Earnest, Jesus was the One Who lived the perfect life we couldn't live, and gave the perfect sacrifice we couldn't give. We can't do enough good things to get close to God. So, basically, Jesus did it for us—it's like you taking the punishment for someone else's crime so that that person can go free. In the same way, our Holy God accepted His Holy Son's death for you and me so that we can be free. God wants you to turn from and confess your sins to Him and to trust Jesus' death for your sins to be enough for you to experience a free life—one that isn't in bondage to work and worldly stuff. Jesus wants you to stop being your own lord and surrender to His Lordship in your life."

"For God so loved the world that he gave his one and only Son, that whoever believes in him shall not perish but have eternal life."[22]

"...If you confess with your mouth 'Jesus is Lord,' and believe in your heart that God raised him from the dead, you will be saved."[23]

"To understand His Lordship as well as your new freedom and privileges, God gives His Holy Spirit to teach you. Suddenly you become more aware of Who God is and who you are in this world—which is really His world. He will also give you special abilities—gifts that you didn't have before, and He will show you where you fit with the skills you already have."

"...the Counselor, the Holy Spirit, whom the Father will send in my name, will teach you all things..."[24]

"And as if all that wasn't enough, God brings into your life specially-gifted people to help you understand the teachings of the Bible, God's Word. They are the best coaches. And they don't change with the tide of politics and trends. They're rock-solid truth-tellers who help you stay true to your calling—because He has a specific calling for which He will equip you—and the coaches in your life will validate it—and they'll help you stay on task so you can fulfill it."

"As iron sharpens iron, so one man sharpens another."[25]

"But even if we just look at the physical world, so much of your crisis could've been prevented," she continues, "and here are some ways:

- Exercise—but it has to be intentionally scheduled. It'll help with that gut of yours, but it'll especially help to clarify your thinking and boost your mood.
- Eat a balanced diet, especially with Omega-3 fatty acids, like flaxseed oil, walnuts, and fish. You can find more information from many online resources regarding other helpful foods.
- Practice good sleep habits. Ideally, without your phone next to you. 'Seventy-five percent of people sleep next to their phones.'[26] At least delegate—which I mentioned earlier—someone who can take a call for you once in a while if that's an issue.

- Ask for help. We also talked about this, but to go a little further, your hints here and there had no urgency about them. You need to assertively re-claim your time away from work for the sake of your mental and physical health. You may even have to tell others how they can help you. Here are some good starters:
  o Tell them:
    - 'I need you to listen, not give advice.'
    - 'I need you to empathize and validate my concerns, that they're legitimate.'
    - 'Don't ask me, "How can I help, but give me the help it looks like I need, like shopping, yard work, laundry, or other tasks. Just say you'll take care of these things, and know I'll reimburse you. Here's why I say this: I sometimes can't say what I need because things seem so dark for me."'[27]

So there it was, like another Sermon on the Mount, but given by a fearless, faith-filled, truth-telling, lovable kid!

As Clarity finishes, R.D. comes from out of nowhere and runs around them both and beats them back to the descending path. His coat is again full of burrs from the brush. He evades her efforts to catch him, so she will have to try again later.

"*But*," she continues, "It doesn't mean you won't have problems. What it means is that the fears in your life—the many fears that can defeat you—aren't meant for you to struggle with all alone. God enables you to face them by His Spirit, His people, and His angels. Bottom line? He controls our world. So, yup, He's got this, and He wants you to know that *every* problem has a divine solution when you let *Him* help you. So the keyword is *let*. You have to *let* Him help you. And you have to *let* His people help you to be the husband and father you really badly want to be right now."

"The LORD will fight for you; you need only to be still."[28]

"Peace I leave with you; my peace I give you. I do not give to you as the world gives. Do not let your hearts be troubled, and do not be afraid."[29]

"All that the Father gives me will come to me, and whoever comes to me, I will never drive away."[30]

"With practice, you will let Jesus guide you away from focusing on your fears. If you don't *let* Him, you will fall back into the trap of staring at them. You know yourself that the more you look at something ominous, the bigger it becomes. And if you let it fill your mind, you'll cripple yourself again. That's not what Jesus wants for you. That's why we're on this path together."

Earnest steps to the side and sits on a stump. Clarity sits on a smaller stump beside him. Looking down at her, he says, "That's what I want. I want to change. I want to be a better husband and a better father. I went to church long ago but eventually went my own way. Now I want His way. I want Him to lead me. My way hasn't worked. I can't lose anything more. I've hit the bottom and hit the wall at the same time. But I'm ready for Jesus to help me out of this. And I'd like to have someone like you to coach me—someone who's not afraid of how I'd react. Someone who genuinely cares about me as a person."

"A friend loves at all times, and a brother is born for adversity."[31]

Clarity hugs him again. "I'm so glad," she says, then, "I have a few more things to show you. Let's go."

8

The Dark Tunnel

Their path leads into the valley. The once bright greens surrounding the path become darker. They enter a tunnel, and only a tiny speck of light is visible in the distance. Clarity keeps the lead.

"Why are we here?" asks Earnest.

The tunnel narrows. The smell of wet soil overwhelms him to the point of nausea.

"This," says Clarity, "is what it's like when you feel as if there are no choices in your life. It's confining, isn't it? Maybe it even feels familiar?"

"But as we keep moving forward, we have light again. So this darkness is only temporary—like the troubles you have had and will have in your life. They are light and momentary. If you are overwhelmed by them, you'll stall out in the middle of them because you let them overwhelm you and allow yourself no options. And sometimes, it's hard to believe daylight is coming. That's why we need people we trust to move us through the rough times and get us back into the light."

"Sometimes, though," continues Clarity, "the desire to persevere fades out mid-tunnel. So, if you get to the point where you're thinking about hurting yourself, the Suicide Prevention Help Line is available." She hands Earnest a wristband that says, 'My story isn't over yet.' On the other side is written a phone number, 1-800-273-8255.

Earnest puts the wristband on. "Thanks. I don't need it yet. But I've come pretty close."

"Well, at least keep it for someone else who might," Clarity replies, then says, "Okay, here are some helpful steps. Think of the acrostic, *TASC*:

- *'Tune in:'* Watch for unusual behaviors, and talk about them with your friend—things like sitting away from other people—when they used to be more social. Also, watch for brooding over a negative self-image and failure themes. They might start selling off stuff. In other words, watch for things that don't look normal for them.
- *'Ask:'* Directly ask: "Are you thinking about suicide?"
- *'State:'* Seriously talk to them about their value to you and the seriousness of suicide, especially the effects on their family and how those left behind would struggle with guilt.
- *'Connect:'* Ideally, with them beside you, contact the Suicide Prevention Help Line at 1-800-273-

8255. Introduce the responder to your friend. Then hand the phone over to them. The responder will skillfully handle the conversation from there and connect them with community resources, where you can take them. Most of all, you want them safe."[32]

As they nearly reach the other end, Earnest touches the cold, damp soil along the tunnel wall. At intervals, he feels stringy roots when suddenly a beetle snaps at him with its hard wings when he touches it. Moments later, a wispy fluttering passes them both. "Just a bat," says Clarity.

They exit onto a vast, sunlit beach at the shore of the lake they had seen from the cabin above. Beyond them, on the stippled waves, the sailboats traverse back and forth. Some have single pilots; others have crews. Alive in the wind, they speak of simplicity and grace. No sirens here, no planes, not even a motorboat. Just wind and waves and beauty in a hair-tossing breeze.

"What do you see here?"

"Freedom," Earnest quickly responds.

"So, in your life, have you felt free? Have you ever *let* yourself relax? Have you *let* yourself enjoy beauty, talent, and fun? Have you *let* yourself enjoy an athletic event or a good book or a new neighbor? Or do you hear accusations of laziness when you take a moment to refresh?"

Earnest knows that Clarity knows the answer. During a long silence, he sees more sails briskly flap as they enter the water dance. He is mesmerized by the choreography. But he answers, "No and yes. No, I haven't let myself be free; and yes, I feel guilty. Or, I really should say, I *felt* guilty. I'm gonna be making some big changes."

He remembers his sacrifices—of health, relationships, and his personal time—and where he is after it all. Deep in his soul is the awareness that he had paid dearly for his perfectionism.

Earnest quietly ponders staying at the lake forever as Clarity plucks off her shoes and socks and splashes into the water. He sits on the warm sand and watches. Without being demonstrative, she shows him how to play, what freedom can look like. Genuinely childlike, she has no worries, no concerns to stop her sheer pleasure. She splashes R.D. as he darts to the edge, barks, and quickly backs away.

The sails beyond and the silliness nearby are whimsical. This is what families do. But not all. And Earnest is not with his family. They had never done this sort of thing. He or they could be here on the beach or in the water or out there, sailing.

Most importantly, they could all get relief from the stresses of his life. "This is what I want. I needed to be here for this."

Earnest broods about never playing with his family: "When was the last time I played?" Well, there were moments here and there. But they were only moments in the house. And distractions usually kept his mind elsewhere. In fact, if Clarity were not playing, she would tell him, "You don't remember when you had fun last because you weren't there. Your head was somewhere else." And she would be right.

But she did not need to say it because Earnest knows in his spirit that God is having His way with him. His new resolve is now stronger than ever.

He throws off his shoes and joins Clarity. They laugh and splash as R.D. barks at them. He soon finds a piece of driftwood and brings it to the water's edge for Clarity to throw. But as she steps out of the water, she is followed by Earnest, so she hands him the stick to pitch. R.D. loves the long tosses and returns them over and over, sprinting to fetch and happily trotting back for more.

"Earnest," Clarity says, "Remember your commitment to get help. Your work struggle has a solution in the mind of God. By getting help, you're so much closer to the freedom you want, the freedom from your struggle, the freedom to truly enjoy life. So now I want to give you a symbol of that freedom." She hands Earnest a large, red kite with long, flowing tails.

The kite is the usual diamond shape but made of silk and outsizes him. He takes it and lets out the twine. Together they watch it rise quickly in the valley breeze. But suddenly, it lifts Earnest up and away.

He clings tightly and looks back at Clarity and R.D. Laughing excitedly and jumping up and down, she waves as R.D. barks. "Goodbye, Earnest! Don't forget about us!"

Earnest is flying and free! Carried along by his kite, he is suddenly over the valley, where farmers below wave from their tractors, hay bales, and horse paddocks. Clothes flap wildly on their lines. Once massive barns become specks as he floats upward.

He passes the granite-faced mountain. Above the cirrus clouds, the air becomes cooler and thinner. But a joyful and free man has no worries here.

He passes a bald eagle catching an updraft. The raptor spots an unfortunate ferret far below. Oblivious to Earnest's joy, he prepares to dive.

Earnest is now above the cabin and passes through its cherry smoke. The place will always be dear to him because that is where he heard from God.

Next, he soars over the ocean of emerald and blue, spotting the hunters and the hunted. Whale calves snuggle near their mothers as a shiver of sharks stalks them.

In moments Earnest is far above a string of cargo ships spaced miles apart. A group of battleships follows from several miles behind. All are tiny dots in the emerald and blue.

But suddenly, the light and the wind become dark and still. Then Earnest hears quiet laughter.

9

Going Back

The sound of footsteps through leaves awakens Earnest, so he sits up as strollers walk by. The nap was refreshing; but, "I was just flying! I was free!"

The shift from there to here was instant. Usually, changes like this would make him anxious; But he has no burning in his stomach. Re-orienting himself, he reviews his dream.

Clarity was a charming child, a prodigy, a brilliant little friend, an unexpected messenger of Truth. She made Earnest think about how his perfectionism had starved his family. Most importantly, she brought him back to Jesus.

He remembers his commitments: to walk with Jesus and his followers for a more objective view of Earnest's life and to set goals with their help. But he especially wants to reconcile with his family. "Lord Jesus, please help me. Please heal where I've wounded my wife and my kids. Restore what I've stolen through my ignorance and pride."

He wants to play again—the sailboats, the beach, splashing in the water with Clarity while R.D. ran around—in those brief moments, Earnest re-discovered the sense of wholeness that comes with play.

The kite reinforced his lessons from Clarity. It carried him, if only briefly, to the excitement of freedom. He is not bound, except as he *chooses*. It also gave him a sense of God's infinite scope, power, love, and enabling Presence. He will listen to God and those whom He has sent to come alongside him. He will let someone hold him accountable to his commitments to family, friends, and a truth-based view of his job.

Earnest will pursue God's path for him. He will prayerfully look for a godly coach who will hear his story. And, of course, he will replay for everyone his amazing dream, so full of conviction, mercy, and grace.

With musing done, Earnest sees an old man on a bench nearby. His long, grey hair falls over his collar. Hunched over a scruffy lap dog, he coos quietly. Then he slowly stands, tucks the dog under his arm, and hobbles toward Earnest.

Somehow the dog and Earnest know each other. They lock eyes, and the dog wags his tail eagerly as the old man shuffles along.

"Know anyone who wants a dog?" he asks with a thinning voice. "It's my granddaughter's, but she's going to another state, and her parents said she can't take him. So I have him, but now I need to move. And where I'm going, they don't allow dogs. R.D. needs a good home."

"R.D.?" was all Earnest could say, then, "I've seen him before!" R.D. sniffs his hand and wags his tail again while Earnest rubs under his chin.

R.D. is his connection to Clarity. He ponders how all this could happen. The old man's weathered, red face and yellowed, sagging eyes plead for Earnest to accept the offer.

Then the old man's eyes fill with tears. His only companion is going to a total stranger.

"Really?" asks Earnest, feeling his eyes well up. "Are you sure? Just like that? Can I give you something for him?"

The old man slowly hands R.D. to Earnest.

R.D.'s tongue is all over his friend's face. He snuggles against his chest as if he had always known him. The old man would not take money. "Just be sure he has a good home."

Then he says, "I can't take this, but I have to do it. Now I need to go." He turns away and tries to step quickly toward the gate, his cane barely tapping the path as he shuffles with baggy pants dragging.

Quickly Earnest thinks, *Could this be Clarity's grandpa?* So he calls out to him, "Sir, you'll think this is a crazy question, but I have to ask you: Is your granddaughter's name Clarity?"

"Yep," he replies, pausing to turn slightly. "Why do you ask?"

"Well, I just had a dream, and in it was a little girl— she was seven-and-a-half years old. She said she was sent to me..."

"Oh?" said the old man, with a half-hearted chuckle. "Wow, God works in mysterious ways, doesn't He?"

"Yeah, He sure does!" But the old man turns away and keeps walking toward the gate. Chat was the furthest thing from his mind.

"You know what?" Earnest tells the dog, "We've both been rescued!"

With R.D. tucked under his arm, Earnest returns to the gate.

"Oh, what a morning! But, wait! I have to get to work!"

He sets R.D. down and grabs his phone to call his boss when he notices: It's Sunday! "I don't have to work today!" Then he says, "Oh, R.D., how do I tell others about all this? They're going to think I'm nuts!"

With his scruffy buddy snuggled against his chest, Earnest returns home. No one is awake yet. But at the start of their day, they will meet a new husband, a new dad, and a new dog.

1 0

Epilogue

A person who is on the verge of burnout struggles with anger, sorrow, depression, and a sense of failure. Reaching a driven perfectionist like Earnest with truthful affirmations of individual worth and alternate choices may initially fall on deaf ears. It is because, for that person inside the struggle, truth takes a long time to take root in what had been hardened by deception and woundedness. The speaker may be sincere and accurate, but the message is often taken only as a gesture of kindness. Bottom line—for a while, anyway—is that the struggler's brooding over failure and exhaustion often blocks out the help that is needed. So it takes an epiphany, as well as moments of self-awareness and vulnerability, for the struggler to let the drawbridge down for a caring coach to enter their life. Extraordinary patience, unconditional love, and persevering prayer are keys to your getting across that bridge. Once you are across, you have a powerful influence. Do not give up! Like Clarity, you can take one more person off the list of burnout casualties and lead them to freedom. For every Earnest, there is someone who wants to help him/her soar to break away to a peaceful, joyful life. God's richest blessings to you if you are that person!

"May the God of hope fill you with all joy and peace as you trust in him, so that you may overflow with hope by the power of the Holy Spirit."[33]

Bibliography

Allen, David. *Getting Things Done: The Art of Stress-free Productivity*. Rev. ed. New York: Penguin Books, 2015.

Amen, Daniel G. *The End of Mental Illness: How Neuroscience is Transforming Psychiatry and Helping Prevent or Reverse Mood and Anxiety Disorders, ADHD, Addictions, PTSD, Psychosis, Personality Disorders, and More.* Carol Stream, IL: Tyndale Momentum, 2020.

Anderson, Neil. *The Steps to Freedom in Christ: A Biblical Guide to Help You Resolve Personal and Spiritual Conflicts and Become a Fruitful Disciple of Jesus.* 4th ed. Bloomington, MN: Bethany House Publishers, 2017.

Boyes, Alice. "How to Stop Obsessing Over Your Mistakes." *Harvard Business Review* (February 25, 2019): n.p. https://hbr.org/2019/02/how-to-stop-obsess-ing-over-your-mistakes.

Comer, John Mark. *The Ruthless Elimination of Hurry: How to Stay Emotional Healthy and Spiritually Alive in the Chaos of the Modern World.* London: Hodder & Stoughton (2019) xiv, 7, 49, 228.

Etherson, Marianne E. "Portraying a False Self: Perfectionism and Inauthenticity." *Psychology Today* (January 30, 2020): n.p. psychologytoday.com.

Fraga, Juli. "A Guide to Burnout." *Healthline* (May 18, 2019): n.p. https://healthline.com/health/tips-for-identifying-and-preventing-burnout.

LivingWorks Education. (2020): n.p. www.livingworks.net.

Mayo Clinic. "Job Burnout and How to Take Action." n.d., n.p. www.mayoclinic.org>burnout>art-20046642.

Moss, Jennifer. "Burnout is About Your Workplace, Not Your People." *Harvard Business Review* (December 11, 2019): n.p. https://hbr.org/2019/12/burnout-is-about-your-workplace-not-your-people.

National Taskforce for Humanity in Healthcare. Position Paper: "The Business Case for Humanity in Healthcare. (April, 2018): n.p. https://www.vocera.com/public/pdf/NTHBusinessCase_final.pdf.

Sandoiu, Ana. "How Perfectionism Affects Your (Mental) Health. *Medical News Today* (October 12, 2018): n.p. medicalnewstoday.com/articles/323323.

The Holy Bible, New International Version. Grand Rapids: Zondervan Bible Publishers, 1996. First published 1973 by International Bible Society.

Vaden, Rory. *Procrastinate on Purpose.* New York: Perigee (2015): 213.

World Health Organization. "Burn-out an Occupational Phenomenon: International Classification of Diseases" (May 28, 2019): n.p. who.int/news/item/28-05-2019-burnout-an-occupational-phenomenon.

About the Author

Kim Douglas Hiltunen, MRE, MBA, RN, is a retired healthcare worker whose admitted stubbornness catalyzed his burnout. Now a recovering perfectionist, he writes from experience, research, and passion to warn of the deadly consequences of sacrificing the joys of family life for the mirage of perfect achievement.

Endnotes

1   Proverbs 8:1,2. *The Holy Bible, New International Version.* Grand Rapids: Zondervan Bible Publishers, 1996. First published 1973 by International Bible Society.

2   World Health Organization. "Burn-out an Occupational Phenomenon: International Classification of Diseases" (May 28, 2019): Retrieved December 21, 2020 from who.int/news/item/28-05-2019-burn-out-an-occupational-phenomenon.

3   Jennifer Moss, "Burnout is About Your Workplace, Not Your People," *Harvard Business Review* (December 11, 2019): Retrieved January 17, 2021 from https://hbr.org/2019/burnout-is-about-your-workplace-not-your-people.

4   National Taskforce for Humanity in Healthcare, Position Paper, "The Business Case for Humanity in Healthcare" (April, 2018): n.p. Retrieved January 17, 2021 from https://www.vocera.com/public/pdf/NTHBusinessCase_final003.pdf.

5   National Taskforce, "The Business Case for Humanity in Healthcare," n.p.

6   John 10:10, NIV.

7   John Mark Comer, *The Ruthless Elimination of*

Hurry: How to Stay Emotionally Healthy and Spiritually Alive in the Chaos of the Modern World (London: Hodder & Stoughton, 2019), xiv.

8 Alice Boyes, "How to Stop Obsessing Over Your Mistakes," *Harvard Business Review* (February 25, 2019); n.p. Retrieved April 2, 2021 from hbr.org/2019/02/how-to-stop-obsessing-over-your-mistakes.

9 Ana Sandoiu, "How Perfectionism Affects Your (Mental) Health," *Medical News Today* (October 12, 2018); n.p. Retrieved January 17, 2021 from medicalnewstoday.com/articles/323323.

10 Marianne E. Etherson, "Portraying a False Self: Perfectionism and Inauthenticity," *Psychology Today* (January 30, 2020); n.p. Retrieved January 17, 2021 from https://psychologytoday.com.

11 Juli Fraga, "A Guide to Burnout," *Healthline* (May 18, 2019); n.p. Retrieved January18,2021 from https://healthline.com/health/tips-for-identifying-and-preventing-burnout.

12 Fraga, "A Guide to Burnout," n.p

13 Comer, *The Ruthless Elimination of Hurry*, 7.

14 Comer, *The Ruthless Elimination of Hurry*, 49.

15 Rory Vaden, *Procrastinate on Purpose*, (New York: Perigee, 2015), 213.

16 Psalm 81:10, NIV.

17 Amos 4:13, NIV.

18 Psalm 55:22, NIV.

19 Luke 1:37, NIV.

20 Matthew 7:7, 8, NIV.

21 Isaiah 55:6, NIV.

22 John 3:16, NIV.

23 Romans 10:9, NIV.

24 John 14:26, NIV.

25 Proverbs 27:17, NIV.

26 Comer, *The Ruthless Elimination of Hurry*, 228.
27 Fraga, "A Guide to Burnout," n.p.
28 Exodus 14:14, NIV.
29 John 14:27, NIV.
30 John 6:37, NIV.
31 Proverbs 17:17, NIV.
32 LivingWorks Education (2020), www.livingworks.net.
33 Romans 15:13, NIV.

CPSIA information can be obtained
at www.ICGtesting.com
Printed in the USA
LVHW022113270521
688708LV00013B/623